CAT JOURNAL COPYRIGHT   1ST PROOF   01/05/93

Canadian representatives: General Publishing Co., Ltd.,
30 Lesmill Road, Don Mills, Ontario M3B 2T6.

International representatives: Worldwide Media Services, Inc.,
30 Montgomery Street, Jersey City, New Jersey 07302.

9 8 7 6 5 4 3 2
Digit on the right indicates the number of this printing.

ISBN 1-56138-094-6

Cover design by Toby Schmidt
Interior design by Christian Benton
Front cover illustration: *Kitten on Cushions* by Sally Holmes, courtesy of Camden Graphics.
Interior illustrations credits: title page: H. Armstrong Roberts; p. 9: H. Armstrong Roberts; p. 16: The Free Library of
Philadelphia Prints and Pictures Department; p. 23: © Jim Channel of Bernard Thornton Artists, London; p. 30:
Royle Publications Ltd., London; p. 32: John Gilroy/Royle Publications Ltd., London; p. 37: H. Armstrong Roberts;
p. 44: © Vanessa Cox; p. 51: The Free Library of Philadelphia Prints and Pictures Department; p. 58: H. Armstrong
Roberts; p. 65: The Free Library of Philadelphia Prints and Pictures Department; p. 72: H. Armstrong Roberts; p. 79:
The Free Library of Philadelphia Prints and Pictures Department; p. 86: The Free Library of Philadelphia Prints and
Pictures Department; p. 93: John Gilroy/Royle Publications Ltd., London; p. 100: H. Armstrong Roberts; p. 107: The
Free Library of Philadelphia Prints and Pictures Department; p. 114: H. Armstrong Roberts; p. 121: The Free Library
of Philadelphia Prints and Pictures Department; p. 128: H. Armstrong Roberts; p. 135: H. Armstrong Roberts; p. 142:
H. Armstrong Roberts; p. 147: The Free Library of Philadelphia Prints and Pictures Department; p. 154: H.
Armstrong Roberts; p. 161: The Free Library of Philadelphia Prints and Pictures Department; p. 168: John Gilroy/
Royle Publications Ltd., London; p. 175: H. Armstrong Roberts; p. 182: The Free Library of Philadelphia Prints and
Pictures Department; p. 189: H. Armstrong Roberts; p. 192: H. Armstrong Roberts

Typography: ITC New Baskerville, by Commcor Communications, Philadelphia, Pennsylvania

This book may be ordered by mail from the publisher.
Please add $2.50 for postage and handling.
But try your bookstore first!
Running Press Book Publishers
125 South Twenty-second Street
Philadelphia, Pennsylvania 19103

Cat Journal

Running Press
Philadelphia, Pennsylvania

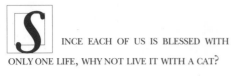

SINCE EACH OF US IS BLESSED WITH ONLY ONE LIFE, WHY NOT LIVE IT WITH A CAT?

ROBERT STEARNS
AMERICAN WRITER

. . . *a* MORNING KISS, A DISCREET TOUCH OF HIS NOSE LANDING SOMEWHERE ON THE MIDDLE OF MY FACE. BECAUSE HIS LONG WHITE WHISKERS TICKLED, I BEGAN EVERY DAY LAUGHING.

JANET F. FAURE
AMERICAN WRITER

ATS ARE INTENDED TO TEACH US THAT
NOT EVERYTHING IN NATURE HAS A FUNCTION.

GARRISON KEILLOR
AMERICAN WRITER

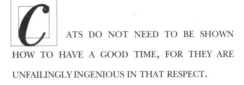

CATS DO NOT NEED TO BE SHOWN HOW TO HAVE A GOOD TIME, FOR THEY ARE UNFAILINGLY INGENIOUS IN THAT RESPECT.

JAMES MASON
ENGLISH ACTOR

*N*O TAME ANIMAL HAS LOST LESS OF ITS
NATIVE DIGNITY OR MAINTAINED MORE OF ITS
ANCIENT RESERVE [THAN] . . . THE CAT.

WILLIAM CONWAY
AMERICAN WRITER

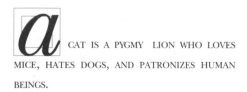

A CAT IS A PYGMY LION WHO LOVES MICE, HATES DOGS, AND PATRONIZES HUMAN BEINGS.

OLIVER HERFORD
AMERICAN HUMORIST AND WRITER

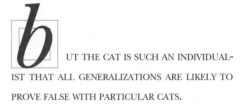

*b*UT THE CAT IS SUCH AN INDIVIDUAL-
IST THAT ALL GENERALIZATIONS ARE LIKELY TO
PROVE FALSE WITH PARTICULAR CATS.

SIDNEY DENHAM
AMERICAN WRITER

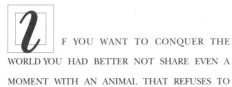 F YOU WANT TO CONQUER THE WORLD YOU HAD BETTER NOT SHARE EVEN A MOMENT WITH AN ANIMAL THAT REFUSES TO BE CONQUERED AT ANY PRICE, BY ANYONE.

DESMOND MORRIS
ENGLISH ZOOLOGIST AND WRITER

...*i*T IS ONLY THE ARTISTIC NATURE, THE TRULY AESTHETIC SOUL THAT APPRECIATES POETRY, AND GRACE, AND ALL REFINED BEAUTY, WHO TRULY LOVES CATS.

HELEN M. WINSLOW
AMERICAN WRITER

HE CAT HAS TOO MUCH SPIRIT TO
HAVE NO HEART.

ERNEST MENAULT
FRENCH WRITER

*I*F ANIMALS COULD SPEAK, THE DOG WOULD BE A BLUNDERING, OUTSPOKEN, HONEST FELLOW—BUT THE CAT WOULD HAVE THE RARE GRACE OF NEVER SAYING A WORD TOO MUCH.

PHILIP GILBERT HAMERTON
ENGLISH WRITER

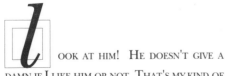

*l*OOK AT HIM! HE DOESN'T GIVE A DAMN IF I LIKE HIM OR NOT. THAT'S MY KIND OF PET.

CARSTEN STROUD
CANADIAN WRITER

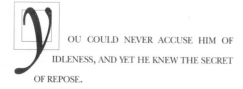

_Y_OU COULD NEVER ACCUSE HIM OF
IDLENESS, AND YET HE KNEW THE SECRET
OF REPOSE.

CHARLES DUDLEY WARNER
AMERICAN WRITER AND EDITOR

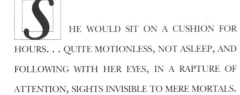HE WOULD SIT ON A CUSHION FOR HOURS. . . QUITE MOTIONLESS, NOT ASLEEP, AND FOLLOWING WITH HER EYES, IN A RAPTURE OF ATTENTION, SIGHTS INVISIBLE TO MERE MORTALS.

Théophile Gautier
French writer and critic

. . . *i* LEARNED FROM MY CAT [TO] GO BAREFOOT, OBEY INSTINCTS, [AND] CLAIM YOUR OWN CHAIR.

SUZY BECKER
AMERICAN WRITER

... **S**HE THINKS OF IT AS HER CHAIR, NO MATTER WHO'S IN IT. THE PERSON MATTERS VERY LITTLE. IT'S LIKE AN EXTRA CUSHION ON THE CHAIR.

GAIL GODWIN
AMERICAN WRITER

 ... *a* CREATURE WHOSE IDEA OF A
GOOD TIME IS TO WALK ACROSS MY FACE WHILE I
AM SLEEPING.

D.L. Stewart
American writer

*N*O ANIMAL SHOULD EVER JUMP UP ON
THE DINING-ROOM FURNITURE UNLESS ABSO-
LUTELY CERTAIN THAT HE CAN HOLD HIS OWN IN
THE CONVERSATION.

FRAN LEBOWITZ
AMERICAN WRITER AND CRITIC

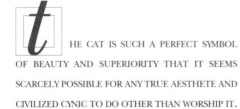

*t*HE CAT IS SUCH A PERFECT SYMBOL
OF BEAUTY AND SUPERIORITY THAT IT SEEMS
SCARCELY POSSIBLE FOR ANY TRUE AESTHETE AND
CIVILIZED CYNIC TO DO OTHER THAN WORSHIP IT.

H.P. LOVECRAFT
AMERICAN WRITER

*a*T BOTTOM, CATS ARE LIKE MUSIC.
THE REASONS FOR THEIR APPEAL TO US CAN
NEVER BE EXPRESSED TOO CLEARLY.

LLOYD ALEXANDER
AMERICAN WRITER

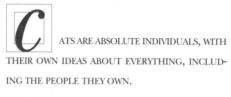

ATS ARE ABSOLUTE INDIVIDUALS, WITH THEIR OWN IDEAS ABOUT EVERYTHING, INCLUDING THE PEOPLE THEY OWN.

JOHN DINGMAN
AMERICAN WRITER

. . . EVER WEAR ANYTHING THAT
PANICS THE CAT.

P.J. O'ROURKE
AMERICAN WRITER

*I*T DOESN'T DO TO BE SENTIMENTAL ABOUT CATS; THE BEST ONES DON'T RESPECT YOU FOR IT. . . .

SUSAN HOWATCH
ENGLISH WRITER

O RESPECT THE CAT IS THE BEGIN-
NING OF THE AESTHETIC SENSE.

ERASMUS DARWIN
ENGLISH POET AND PHYSIOLOGIST

HERE ARE TWO MEANS OF REFUGE
FROM THE MISERIES OF LIFE: MUSIC AND CATS.

ALBERT SCHWEITZER
FRENCH PHYSICIAN AND PHILOSOPHER

*h*IS TENDER CALL WAKES NOT ALARM,

BUT THOUGH HE GROWL OR SOFTLY SOUND,

STILL IS HIS VOICE RICH AND PROFOUND—

THERE LIES HIS SECRET AND HIS CHARM.

CHARLES PIERRE BAUDELAIRE
FRENCH WRITER AND CRITIC

. . . THAT . . . CAT PURRS LIKE A WINDMILL, LIKE AN ELECTRIC CAR, LIKE A TEA-KETTLE, LIKE A WHOLE BOILED DINNER.

HARRIET PRESCOTT SPOFFORD
AMERICAN WRITER

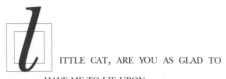

ITTLE CAT, ARE YOU AS GLAD TO
HAVE ME TO LIE UPON

As I AM TO FEEL YOUR FUR UNDER MY HAND?

AMY LOWELL
AMERICAN POET

HE PURR OF A CAT ON A LAP MAKES SOLITUDE ENDURABLE.

MURIEL BEADLE
AMERICAN WRITER

*h*ER LITTLE CAT SOUL IMPLORED SOME
COMPANY, SOME FRIENDSHIP IN A LONELY
WORLD.

PIERRE LOTI
FRENCH WRITER

*A*RE CATS LAZY? WELL, MORE POWER TO THEM IF THEY ARE. WHICH ONE OF US HAS NOT ENTERTAINED THE DREAM OF DOING JUST AS HE LIKES, WHEN AND HOW HE LIKES, AND AS MUCH AS HE LIKES?

FERNAND MÉRY
FRENCH WRITER

*t*O BE REMINDED THAT ONE IS VERY MUCH LIKE OTHER MEMBERS OF THE ANIMAL KINGDOM IS OFTEN FUNNY. . . THOUGH. . . I DO NOT TOO MUCH MIND BEING SOMEWHAT LIKE A CAT. . . .

JOSEPH WOOD KRUTCH
AMERICAN WRITER

*C*ATS ONLY OCCUPY SPACE AND THINK ABOUT THREE THINGS: FOOD, SEX, AND NOTHING. IF THEY'RE NEUTERED, THAT LEAVES FOOD.

PENNY WARD MOSER
AMERICAN WRITER

HEY'RE THE MOST GRACEFUL, SINU-
OUS, SEXY, TRULY SENSUOUS CREATURES IN THE
WORLD.
CAROL LAWRENCE
AMERICAN DANCER AND ACTRESS

[*t* HE CATS] HAD FINISHED THEIR THREE-HOUR MORNING NAP AND HAD NOT YET SETTLED DOWN FOR THEIR FOUR-HOUR AFTERNOON SIESTA.

LILIAN JACKSON BRAUN
AMERICAN WRITER

*h*E'S VERY LIGHT WHEN HE LIES ON YOUR KNEES, AND VERY HEAVY WHEN I CARRY HIM INTO THE KITCHEN IN THE EVENINGS TO PREVENT HIM FROM SLEEPING ON MY BED.

COLETTE
FRENCH WRITER

*h*E LIES THERE, PURRING AND DREAM-
ING, SHIFTING HIS LIMBS NOW AND THEN IN AN
ECSTASY OF CUSHIONED COMFORT. HE SEEMS
THE INCARNATION OF EVERYTHING SOFT AND SILKY
AND VELVETY, WITHOUT A SHARP EDGE IN HIS
COMPOSITION, A DREAMER WHOSE PHILOSOPHY IS
SLEEP AND LET SLEEP. . . .

SAKI
ENGLISH WRITER

NE OF THE WAYS IN WHICH CATS

SHOW HAPPINESS IS BY SLEEPING.

CLEVELAND AMORY
AMERICAN WRITER

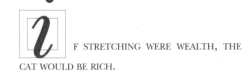

F STRETCHING WERE WEALTH, THE CAT WOULD BE RICH.

AFRICAN PROVERB

*t*HERE IS NO PRETENCE OF SYMPATHY ABOUT THE CAT. HE LIVES ALONE, ALOFT, SUBLIME, IN A WISE PASSIVENESS. HE IS EXCESSIVELY PROUD, AND, WHEN HE IS MADE THE SUBJECT OF CONVERSATION, WILL CAST ONE GLANCE OF SCORN, AND LEAVE THE ROOM IN WHICH PERSONALITIES ARE BANDIED.

ANDREW LANG
SCOTTISH POET AND SCHOLAR

... *h*UMAN BEINGS, FOR ONE REASON OR ANOTHER, MAY HIDE THEIR FEELINGS, BUT A CAT DOES NOT.

ERNEST HEMINGWAY
AMERICAN WRITER

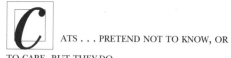

CATS . . . PRETEND NOT TO KNOW, OR TO CARE, BUT THEY DO.

COLIN EISLER
AMERICAN WRITER

NEVER HIRE ANYONE MY CAT DOESN'T
APPROVE OF.

ROSEMARY SIMPSON
AMERICAN WRITER

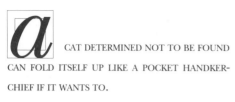 CAT DETERMINED NOT TO BE FOUND CAN FOLD ITSELF UP LIKE A POCKET HANDKER-CHIEF IF IT WANTS TO.

Dr. Louis J. Camuti
American writer

 CAT IMPROVES THE GARDEN WALL IN SUNSHINE, AND THE HEARTH IN FOUL WEATHER.

JUDITH MERKLE RILEY
AMERICAN WRITER

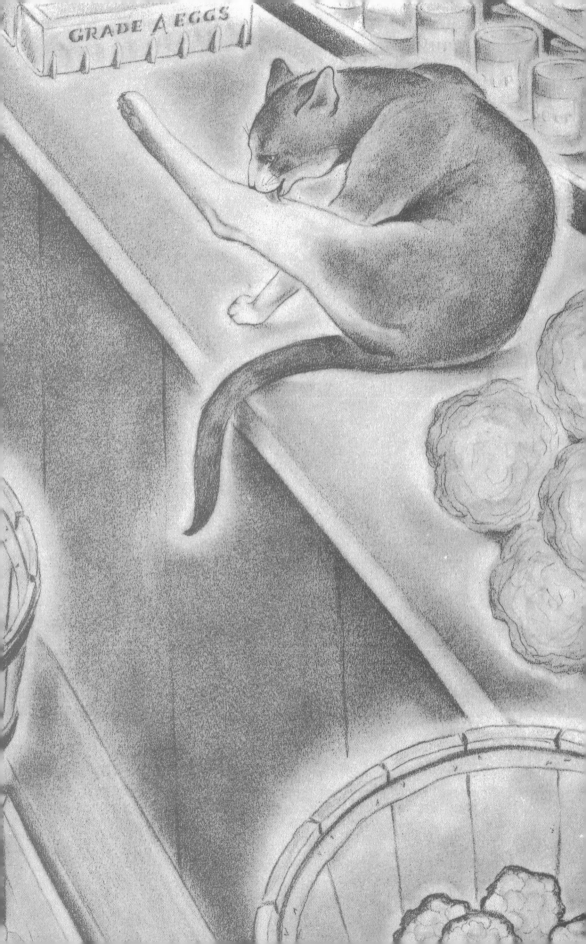

*I*N THESE DAYS OF TENSION, HUMAN BEINGS CAN LEARN A GREAT DEAL ABOUT RELAXATION FROM WATCHING A CAT, WHO DOESN'T JUST LIE DOWN WHEN IT IS TIME TO REST, BUT POURS HIS BODY ON THE FLOOR AND RESTS IN EVERY NERVE AND MUSCLE.

MURRAY ROBINSON
AMERICAN WRITER

ATS AMONG THEMSELVES JUDGE EACH
OTHER EXACTLY AS WE JUDGE THEM.

GEORGE CUVIER
FRENCH ZOOLOGIST

*t*HEY TAUGHT THE CHILDREN THE LESSON OF THE NECESSITY OF KINDNESS TO SMALLER, WEAKER CREATURES. BUT MOSTLY THEY WERE JUST THERE: WARM BREATH, FURRY LIVES, ACUTE INTELLIGENCE, CARRIERS OF OPTIMISM AND FAITH, FOR WHILE THEY SEEMED NEVER WHOLLY CONVINCED OF MAN'S WISDOM, THEY STILL, WITH THE TRUST OF THEIR LIVES, GAVE HIM THE BENEFIT OF THE DOUBT.

NANCY THAYER
AMERICAN WRITER

i HAVE A KITTEN, MY DEAR, THE
DROLLEST OF ALL CREATURES THAT EVER WORE
A CAT'S SKIN.

WILLIAM COWPER
ENGLISH POET

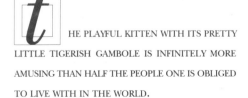

*t*HE PLAYFUL KITTEN WITH ITS PRETTY LITTLE TIGERISH GAMBOLE IS INFINITELY MORE AMUSING THAN HALF THE PEOPLE ONE IS OBLIGED TO LIVE WITH IN THE WORLD.

LADY SYDNEY MORGAN
ENGLISH WRITER

*E*VEN WHEN A KITTEN IS QUIET, HE IS THE DROLLEST OF CREATURES. . . . HIS HEAD, HEAVY WITH SLEEP, HIS OUTSTRETCHED PAWS, HIS AIR OF INEFFABLE LANGUOR, ALL TELL OF COMFORT AND CONTENT.

JULES HUSSON CHAMPFLEURY
FRENCH WRITER

*C*ATS CAN BE VERY FUNNY, AND HAVE THE ODDEST WAYS OF SHOWING THEY'RE GLAD TO SEE YOU.

W.H. AUDEN
ENGLISH POET

T ALWAYS GIVES ME A SHIVER WHEN I
SEE A CAT SEEING WHAT I CAN'T SEE.

ELEANOR FARJEON
ENGLISH WRITER

WHAT SORT OF PHILOSOPHERS ARE WE, WHO KNOW NOTHING OF THE ORIGIN AND DES-TINY OF CATS?

HENRY DAVID THOREAU
AMERICAN NATURALIST AND WRITER

ATS LET US ALONE WHEN THEY DO
NOT UNDERSTAND US.

ANNE MENDELSON
AMERICAN WRITER

*P*ERHAPS IT IS BECAUSE CATS DO NOT
LIVE BY HUMAN PATTERNS, DO NOT FIT
THEMSELVES INTO PRESCRIBED BEHAVIOR,
THAT THEY ARE SO UNITED TO CREATIVE PEOPLE.

ANDRE NORTON
AMERICAN WRITER

. . . **C**ATS ARE THE WISE MAN'S BEST COMPANIONS, FOR THEY RESPECT HIS STUDIOUS HOURS.

ANATOLE FRANCE
FRENCH WRITER

HERE ARE PEOPLE WHO LIKE TO BE ALONE WHEN THEY READ AND PEOPLE WHO PREFER THE COMPANY OF CATS.

GEORGIA DULLEA
AMERICAN WRITER

C ATS ARE LUXURIOUS AND THEY MAKE US FEEL LUXURIOUS. . . . PERHAPS THEY ARE SYMBOLS OF MAN'S INEFFABLE ARTISTIC LONGINGS.

ROGER CARAS
AMERICAN WRITER

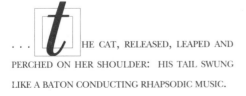

. . . HE CAT, RELEASED, LEAPED AND
PERCHED ON HER SHOULDER: HIS TAIL SWUNG
LIKE A BATON CONDUCTING RHAPSODIC MUSIC.

TRUMAN CAPOTE
AMERICAN WRITER

VERY CAT KNOWS THAT THE IDEAL
. . . HOUSE SHOULD HAVE BOTH AN ATTIC AND A
CELLAR, THE ATTIC FOR FUN AND GAMES, THE
CELLAR FOR HUNTING.

MAY SARTON
AMERICAN WRITER

*W*HY, IT IS ASKED, SHOULD WE HUMBLE OURSELVES TO WIN THE FLUCTUATING AFFECTIONS OF A CAT. . . WHY INDEED SAVE THAT SOME OF US MOST DESIRE THAT WHICH IS DIFFICULT TO OBTAIN. . . .

AGNES REPPLIER
AMERICAN WRITER

CATS HAVE MAGIC, BUT IN STUBBORN CASES IT TAKES A LITTLE TIME FOR THEIR MAGIC TO MAKE ITSELF FELT.

JESSAMYN WEST
AMERICAN WRITER

THE CAT DOES NOT NEGOTIATE WITH THE MOUSE.

ROBERT K. MASSIE
AMERICAN WRITER

*t*HE CAT STAYED WITH US FIVE DAYS. AFTER THOSE FIVE DAYS NO MICE APPEAR. THE CAT THEN LEAVES US AND THE MICE NEVER COME BACK. I HAVE NEVER KNOWN BEFORE OR SINCE SUCH A PROFESSIONAL CAT.

AGATHA CHRISTIE
ENGLISH WRITER

*O*NCE YOU HAVE BEEN PRESENTED WITH A MOUSE BY YOUR CAT, YOU WILL NEVER BE THE SAME EVER AGAIN. SHE CAN USE YOU FOR A DOORMAT. AND SHE WILL, TOO.

PAUL GALLICO
AMERICAN JOURNALIST AND WRITER

 . . . SAYING "EITHER THOSE CATS GO OR I GO" MAY BE WORDS YOU'LL REGRET.

ERIC GURNEY
AMERICAN WRITER

*t*HE MOON GETS UP AND NIGHT COMES, HE IS THE CAT THAT WALKS BY HIMSELF, AND ALL PLACES ARE ALIKE TO HIM. THEN HE GOES OUT TO THE WET WILD WOODS OR UP ON THE WET WILD TREES OR ON THE WET WILD ROOFS, WAVING HIS WILD TAIL AND WALKING BY HIS WILD LONE.

RUDYARD KIPLING
ENGLISH WRITER

HE SOUL OF ANOTHER IS A MYSTERY,
AND A CAT'S SOUL EVEN MORE SO.

ANTON CHEKHOV
RUSSIAN WRITER